Contents

Dear Learner:

This little workbook is here to give you extra practice with long-vowel words. Turn to it each time you complete a new title. Answering the comprehension questions and doing the activities will help you become a super-strong reader, writer, and speller.

Happy Learning!
Your Friends at Scholastic

Comprehension Questions

NOTE TO CAREGIVER: After your child reads a book, invite him/her to answer the three comprehension questions. To extend learning, challenge your child to create original story-related questions to ask you!

A Cake for Dave (long a: a_e)

1. What special things do Kate, Wade, and Jane give Dave for his birthday?
2. What happens at the end of the story?
3. How do you celebrate your birthday? Talk about it.

Queen Bee (long e: ee)

1. What does Dee dream about? Are her dreams happy or sad?
2. What lesson does Dee learn at the end of the story?
3. Would you like to be a bee? Why or why not?

Nice, Nice Mice (long i: i_e)

1. Ike and Mike are nice. Can you think of more words to describe them?
2. What nice thing do Ike and Mike do for their pals?
3. What nice things can you do for your pals? Talk about it.

A Mole Home (long o: o_e)

1. What three things does Cole see that would NOT make a good home for a mole? Why?
2. Cole sees a note. What does it tell him to do?
3. Do the stones lead Cole to a good home for a mole? Why or why not?

A Tune for Mule (long u: u_e)

1. What happens when Mule says, "Dute-a-lute-tute!"?
2. Does the story have a happy ending? Why or why not?
3. Is this story nonfiction (real) or fiction (pretend)? How do you know?

Gail and Kait (long a: ai)

1. What things do Gail and Kait do in the rain?
2. Do Gail's feelings about rain change at the end of the story? How do you know?
3. What do you like to do when it rains? Talk about it.

Dean and Jean (long e: ea)

1. Who are the characters in this story? Where does it take place?
2. What lesson does Jean learn from the book that Dean reads to her?
3. Why is it important to say "Please" and "Sorry"? Talk about it.

Goat and Big Mean Toad (long o: oa)

1. At the beginning of the story, why can't Goat roam on the road?
2. Why does Big Mean Toad agree to take Goat on his boat?
3. Is Big Mean Toad *really* mean? Talk about it.

Joan's Tea Time (long vowels)

1. Do you remember all the things Joan does to get ready for her tea party? Give it a try.
2. What is surprising about Peet, Joan's tea party guest?
3. Would you like to have a tea party? Who would you invite?

The Sea Race (long vowels)

1. Where does this race take place? Who is racing?
2. Is Eel fast? Why does Eel win the race?
3. How is this story like *The Tortoise and the Hare*? How is it different?

Abe and Zeek (long vowels)

1. What rule does Abe make about playing with Zeek?
2. Why does Zeek get mad at Abe?
3. What happens at the end of the story? Talk about it.

Five Nice Beans (long vowels)

1. Do you remember all the things the five beans do during their day? Give it a try.
2. Do the beans' feelings about the huge ride change when they are on it? How do you know?
3. How are the five beans like people? How are they different?

Long-Vowel Sound Review 1

NOTE TO CAREGIVER: Challenge your child to read each word and match it to the right picture. TIP: If he/she struggles, review long-vowel sounds.

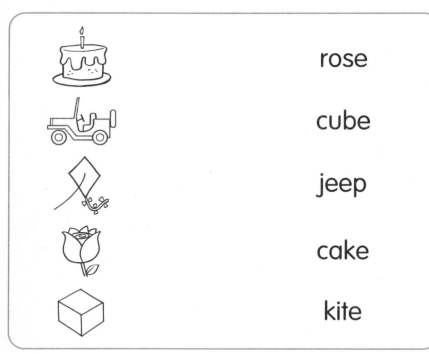

rose

cube

jeep

cake

kite

Long-Vowel Sound Review 2

NOTE TO CAREGIVER: Challenge your child to read each word and match it to the right picture. TIP: If he/she struggles, review long-vowel sounds.

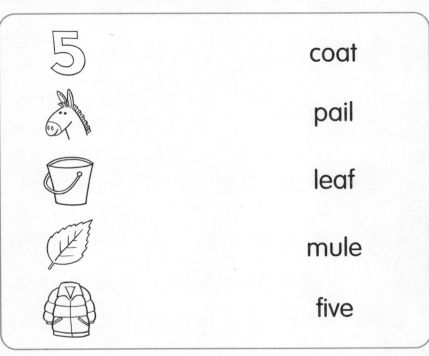

coat

pail

leaf

mule

five

A Cake for Dave

Review the sound.

long *a*: *a_e*		cake

Circle the words.

cake   late   game   wave   ape

r b o c a k e j d u w m
g a m e p z i q a p e x
n w a v e n u l a t e m

Practice
Read, trace, and write the words.

cake cake

late late

game game

wave wave

ape ape

Queen Bee

Review the sound.

long e: ee		bee

Circle the words.

bee   see   eel   jeep   peek

p e e k o w b e e r a x
z a h w s e e c u f g i
y j e e p m o r v e e l

Practice
Read, trace, and write the words.

bee b̶e̶e̶

see s̶e̶e̶

eel e̶e̶l̶

jeep j̶e̶e̶p̶

peek p̶e̶e̶k̶

Nice, Nice Mice

Review the sound.

long *i*: *i_e*		mice

Circle the words.

mice ride bike time fine

t i m e j u b i k e n r

p f i n e l x a t g e v

a m i c e y u q r i d e

Practice
Read, trace, and write the words.

mice mice

ride ride

bike bike

time time

fine fine

A Mole Home

Review the sound.

long *o*: o_e		mole

Circle the words.

mole	home	rose	cone	joke

g b f w o h u j o k e z

a q r o s e h p m o l e

h o m e v x i r c o n e

Practice

Read, trace, and write the words.

mole mole

home home

rose rose

cone cone

joke joke

A Tune for Mule

Review the sound.

long *u*: *u_e*		mule

Circle the words.

mule   cute   huge   tune   dude

p e x g n c u t e p o j
z a m u l e z r d u d e
t u n e k b i v h u g e

Practice
Read, trace, and write the words.

mule mule

cute cute

huge huge

tune tune

dude dude

Gail and Kait

Review the sound.

long *a*: *ai*		rain

Circle the words.

rain	pain	wait	sail	tail

```
o d n g s u t a i l m c
z p a i n s e r a i n b
s a i l k v y w a i t x
```

Practice

Read, trace, and write the words.

rain rain

pain pain

wait wait

sail sail

tail tail

Dean and Jean

Review the sound.

long *e*: *ea*		leaf

Circle the words.

leaf mean seat read deal
r m e a n a d e a l g i
z r e a d u n t s e a t
d k i f l e a f t s r u

Practice

Read, trace, and write the words.

leaf leaf

mean mean

seat seat

read read

deal deal

Goat and Big Mean Toad

Review the sound.

long *o*: *oa*		goat

Circle the words.

goat	toad	boat	soap	roam

```
c t s o a p a g t o a d
b o a t p g u r o a m z
s r e m k y g o a t a l
```

Practice
Read, trace, and write the words.

goat goat

toad toad

boat boat

soap soap

roam roam

Joan's Tea Time

Review the sounds.

long *a*	long *e*	long *i*	long *o*	long *u*
cake	tea	five	rose	huge

Circle the words.

cake   tea   five   rose   huge

i t e a g z h u g e o x
d u c a k e v s o t q e
r o s e a p f i v e u n

Practice
Read, trace, and write the words.

cake cake

tea tea

five five

rose rose

huge huge

The Sea Race

Review the sounds.

long *a*	long *e*	long *i*	long *o*	long *u*
race	eel	time	nose	mule

Circle the words.

race   eel   time   nose   mule

```
r t i m e x o m u l e q
s u r a c e t r i e e l
a p n o s e u t v t a f
```

Practice
Read, trace, and write the words.

race ~race~

eel ~eel~

time ~time~

nose ~nose~

mule ~mule~

Abe and Zeek

Review the sounds.

long *a*	long *e*	long *i*	long *o*	long *u*
HELLO My name is Jane				KEEP OFF GRASS
name	jeep	lime	cone	rule

Circle the words.

name   jeep   lime   cone   rule

q u l i m e a z j e e p

h e z u r o c o n e g r

e n a m e y b i r u l e

Practice

Read, trace, and write the words.

name name

jeep jeep

lime lime

cone cone

rule rule

Five Nice Beans

Review the sounds.

long *a*	long *e*	long *i*	long *o*	long *u*
lake	read	bite	hole	cute

Circle the words.

lake   read   bite   hole   cute

q u c u t e o z g a j p
u d b i t e i z h o l e
q l a k e m i r e a d x

Practice
Read, trace, and write the words.

lake lake

read read

bite bite

hole hole

cute cute

CONGRATULATIONS!

_____
your name

You read 12 long-vowel books & completed this mini-workbook.

You are a **PHONICS STAR!**